MRCP PART 1 PAST TOPICS
A REVISION SYLLABUS

Compiled and edited by

Philip A Kalra MA MB BChir MRCP MD
Consultant Nephrologist
Hope Hospital, The University of Manchester, Salford

Egerton Court, Parkgate Estate, Knutsford, Cheshire
WA16 8DX

First published 1996
Reprinted 1997

ISBN 0 906896 78 9

A catalogue record for this book is available from the British Library.

Text prepared by Breeze Limited, Manchester.
Printed by BPC Wheatons Ltd., Exeter

MRCP PART 1 PAST TOPICS

A REVISION SYLLABUS

CONTENTS

A breakdown of the relative distribution of topics is given below. A slight variation may occur from exam to exam.

Subject Area	**Number of MCQs**
Neurology	5/6
Pharmacology	4/5
Cardiology	4/5
Basic Sciences	3/6
Gastroenterology	4/5
Respiratory Medicine	4
Infectious Diseases	4
Endocrinology	4
Psychiatry	4
Haematology	4
Nephrology	3/4
Metabolism	3
Immunology	2/3
Rheumatology	2
Genetics	1
Statistics	1
Dermatology	0/1
Ophthalmology	0/1
Total Number of MCQs	**60**

INTRODUCTION

The pass rate for candidates sitting the MRCP (UK) Part 1 examination is fixed, such that the top 35% are successful. As there are increasing numbers of entrants for each exam this encourages candidates to develop a highly competitive approach. Furthermore, the style of preparation for the examination is changing with a greater proportion of candidates attending courses that improve MCQ answering technique and question exposure; innumerable books of 'typical' MRCP MCQs are also available, and candidates can be swamped with 'likely topics' for forthcoming exams.

This book is markedly different from all previous Part 1 books, and provides a major advantage to candidates by indicating the topics most frequently used in past Royal College examinations. The material has been accumulated by amalgamating the feedback of candidates who have taken the exam after attending PasTest courses during the last five years (1992–1996).

How to use this book

The material is displayed in 3 ways:

- Topics are listed chronologically within each parent subject.
- Within each subject, topics are listed in order of frequency to give an 'index of most frequent topics'.

These two lists enable candidates to appreciate the spectrum of questions used in any one MRCP examination, and provide insight into topics which may be declining in popularity whilst others may be increasingly utilised (eg. inflammatory/vasoactive mediators), reflecting advances in medical science. The frequency indexes highlight the most important topics within a subject, and should help guide the candidate's revision – eg. within *Nephrology* it would be sensible to concentrate more revision time on the nephrotic syndrome and related membranous/minimal change glomerulonephritis (14 questions during last 5 years) than on renal bone disease (one question during same period). Equally, it should become clear to candidates that prolonged revision of subjects such as *Genetics*, *Ophthalmology* and *Dermatology* (only 1 or 2 questions for all three subjects combined in any one exam) will be less fruitful than concentrating on deficiencies in their knowledge of *Cardiology* and *Neurology* (10–11 questions in any exam).

- The third section within each chapter is a compilation of related topics under subheadings which will provide a comprehensive checklist for candidates that should enhance revision strategy.

There are inevitable overlaps, for example pulmonary manifestations of SLE or rheumatoid arthritis could appear in either of 2 sections; certain topics are cross-referenced. Many 'basic science' topics are also considered within the parent subject, such as renal tubular and respiratory physiology, and the effects of lesions involving/anatomy of cranial and peripheral nerves.

As there is no published syllabus available for this exam I hope that all MRCP Part 1 candidates will benefit from the focused revision that this book will facilitate.

P A Kalra

BASIC SCIENCE: EXAM TOPICS

February 1996

Aldosterone secretion

October 1995

Physiology of late pregnancy

July 1995

Steroid hormone receptors
H_2 receptors
Atrial natriuretic peptide

February 1995

Amyloid plaques
Apolipoprotein
$Alpha_1$-antitrypsin

October 1994

The polymerase chain reaction
Actions of insulin
Endothelium derived relaxing factor (Nitric oxide)
Mitochondrial DNA
The RAS oncogene
Adenosine

February 1994

Somatostatin

October 1993

Oxygen uptake by haemoglobin
Physiology of normal bone
Atrial natriuretic peptide
Actions of insulin

July 1993

Serum ferritin
Angiotensin-II

February 1993

Function of hypothalamic nucleii

February 1992

Neurotransmitters
Physiological changes in normal pregnancy
Prostacyclin

October 1991

Peripheral oedema
Actions of ADH

February 1991

Atrial natriuretic peptide
Insulin resistance

BASIC SCIENCE: TOPIC FREQUENCY INDEX

Actions of insulin	Oct 94, Oct 93, Feb 91
Atrial natriuretic hormone	July 95, Oct 93, Feb 91
Physiology of pregnancy	Oct 95, Feb 92
ADH, actions of	Oct 91
Adenosine	Oct 94
Aldosterone secretion	Feb 96
$Alpha_1$-antitrypsin	Feb 95
Amyloid plaques	Feb 95
Angiotensin II	July 93
Apolipoprotein	Feb 95
Endothelium derived relaxing factor	Oct 94
H_2 receptors	July 95
Hypothalamic nuclei	Feb 93
Mitochondrial DNA	Oct 94
Neurotransmitters	Feb 92
Oxygen uptake by haemoglobin	Oct 93
Peripheral oedema	Oct 91
Physiology of normal bone	Oct 93
Polymerase chain reaction	Oct 94
Prostacyclin	Feb 92
RAS oncogene	Oct 94
Serum ferritin	July 93
Somatostatin	Feb 94
Steroid hormone receptors	July 95

BASIC SCIENCE: REVISION CHECKLIST

Average 3–6 questions per exam (with many other questions involving anatomy/physiology of a specific topic included within that section). Numbers in brackets indicate the relative frequency of topics.

Physiology

- ❑ Changes in pregnancy (2)
- ❑ Haemoglobin function
- ❑ Physiology of bone
- ❑ Aetiology of oedema

Pathology

- ❑ Amyloid plaques

Hormone and mediator biochemistry

- ❑ Atrial natriuretic peptides (3)
- ❑ Insulin/insulin resistance (3)
- ❑ Adenosine
- ❑ ADH
- ❑ Aldosterone
- ❑ Angiotensin
- ❑ EDRF (nitric oxide)
- ❑ H_2 receptors
- ❑ Neurotransmitters
- ❑ Prostacyclin
- ❑ Somatostatin
- ❑ Steroid receptors

Miscellaneous

- ❑ Apolipoproteins
- ❑ $Alpha_1$-antitrypsin
- ❑ Mitochondrial DNA function
- ❑ Oncogenes

February 1996

Prolonged QT syndrome
Massive pulmonary embolism
Constrictive pericarditis
Cannon waves

October 1995

Pulmonary embolism and the pill
Mitral stenosis
Constrictive pericarditis
Wolff-Parkinson-White syndrome
Cardiac effects of alcohol abuse

July 1995

Cardiac complications of alcohol
Wolff-Parkinson-White syndrome
Ostium secundum ASD
Antibiotic prophylaxis of valves

February 1995

Diastolic dysfunction of LV
Fallot's tetralogy
Extension of an MI
Broad complex tachycardia

October 1994

Fixed splitting of the 2nd heart sound
Cyanotic heart disease
Ventricular tachycardia
Pulmonary embolus
Cardiac lesions causing reduced lung markings on chest X-ray

July 1994

Causes of giant 'a' waves in the JVP
Streptokinase therapy following myocardial infarction
Conversion of atrial fibrillation to sinus rhythm
Causes of reversed splitting of the second heart sound
Acute myocardial infarction in the elderly

February 1994

Causes of a dilated cardiomyopathy
Causes of a right/left shunt
Dissection of the aorta
Cardiac tamponade

October 1993

Mitral valve prolapse
Pulmonary hypertension
Cardiac valve lesions
Loud first heart sound
Features resulting from myocardial infarction

July 1993

Uncontrolled atrial fibrillation
Acute pericardial effusion
Mitral stenosis
Features of patent ductus arteriosus

February 1993

Drugs causing torsades des pointes
Aetiology of congestive cardiomyopathy
Acute myocardial infarction
Left bundle branch block
Mitral stenosis
Constrictive pericarditis

October 1992

Prolonged QT syndrome
Unstable angina
Aortic dissection
Cannon 'a' waves in the JVP

July 1992

Wolff-Parkinson-White syndrome
Left ventricular failure
Primary pulmonary hypertension
Constrictive pericarditis

February 1992

Recurrent pulmonary thromboembolism
Ventricular tachycardia
Early diastolic murmur
Giant 'a' waves in the JVP

October 1991

Constrictive pericarditis
Cardiovascular complications of alcohol
Hypertrophic cardiomyopathy

February 1991

Cardiac catheterization data
Infective endocarditis
The coronary circulation
Constrictive pericarditis
Wolff-Parkinson-White syndrome

CARDIOLOGY: TOPIC FREQUENCY INDEX

Constrictive pericarditis	Feb 96, Oct 95, Feb 93, July 92, Oct 91, Feb 91
Cannon 'a' waves in JVP	Feb 96, July 94, Oct 92, Feb 92
Heart sounds	Oct 94, July 94, Oct 93, Feb 92
Myocardial infarction	Feb 95, July 94, Oct 93, Feb 93
Pulmonary embolism	Feb 96, Oct 95, Oct 94, Feb 92
Wolff-Parkinson-White	Oct 95, July 95, July 92, Feb 91
Alcohol abuse, effects of	Oct 95, July 95, Oct 91
Cardiomyopathy	Feb 94, Feb 93, Oct 91
Mitral stenosis	Oct 95, July 93, Feb 93
Ventricular tachycardia	Feb 95, Oct 94, Feb 92
Atrial fibrillation	July 94, July 93
Cardiac valve lesions	Oct 94, Oct 93
Dissection of aorta	Feb 94, Oct 92
Left ventricular failure	Feb 95, July 92
Prolonged QT syndrome	Feb 96, Oct 92
Pulmonary hypertension	Oct 93, July 92
Antibiotic prophylaxis of valves	July 95
Cardiac catheterization	Feb 91
Cardiac tamponade	Feb 94
Coronary circulation	Feb 91
Cyanotic heart disease	Oct 94
Fallot's tetralogy	Feb 95
Left bundle branch block	Feb 93
Mitral valve prolapse	Oct 93
Ostium secundum ASD	July 95
Patent ductus arteriosus	July 93
Pericardial effusion	July 93
Right-left shunt	Feb 94
Torsades des pointes	Feb 93
Unstable angina	Oct 92

CARDIOLOGY: REVISION CHECKLIST

Average 4–5 questions per exam. Numbers in brackets indicate the relative frequency of topics.

Valvular heart disease

- ❑ Heart sounds (4)
- ❑ Mitral stenosis (3)
- ❑ Valve lesions (2)
- ❑ Antibiotic prophylaxis
- ❑ Catheterisation data
- ❑ Mitral valve prolapse

Arrhythmias

- ❑ Wolff-Parkinson-White (4)
- ❑ Ventricular tachycardia (3)
- ❑ Atrial fibrillation (2)
- ❑ Prolonged Q-T (2)
- ❑ LBBB
- ❑ Torsades des pointes

Pericardial disease

- ❑ Constrictive pericarditis (6)
- ❑ Cardiac tamponade
- ❑ Pericardial effusion

IHD/heart muscle disease

- ❑ Myocardial infarction (4)
- ❑ Cardiomyopathy (3)
- ❑ Left ventricular failure (2)
- ❑ Unstable angina

Congenital heart disease

- ❑ Cyanotic heart disease/Eisenmenger's (4)
- ❑ ASD
- ❑ Patent ductus arteriosus
- ❑ VSD

Large vessel disease
- ❑ Pulmonary embolus (4)
- ❑ Aortic dissection (2)
- ❑ Pulmonary hypertension (2)

Miscellaneous
- ❑ Cannon 'a' waves in JVP (4)
- ❑ Alcohol and the heart (3)
- ❑ Coronary circulation

February 1996
Associations with psoriasis

October 1995
Itchy papular rash

February 1995
Causes of pruritus

October 1994
Causes of photosensitivity

July 1993
Features of psoriasis

February 1993
Causes of skin lesions in the limbs

October 1992
Causes of perforating foot ulcers
Alopecia areata

July 1992
Skin manifestations of systemic disease
Photosensitive skin lesions

October 1991
Severe pruritus

February 1991
Erythema multiforme

DERMATOLOGY: TOPIC FREQUENCY INDEX

Photosensitivity	Oct 94, July 92
Pruritus	Feb 95, Oct 91
Psoriasis	Feb 96, July 93
Alopecia areata	Oct 92
Erythema multiforme	Feb 91
Papular rash	Oct 95
Perforating foot ulcers	Oct 92
Skin lesions in limbs	Feb 93
Skin manifestations of systemic disease	July 92

DERMATOLOGY: REVISION CHECKLIST

Average only 1 question each or every other exam. Numbers in brackets indicate the relative frequency of topics.

Specific skin lesions

- ❑ Psoriasis (2)
- ❑ Alopecia areata
- ❑ Erythema multiforme
- ❑ Papular rash

Systemic manifestations

- ❑ Pruritus (2)
- ❑ Photosensitivity (2)
- ❑ Skin manifestations of systemic disease

Miscellaneous

- ❑ Foot ulcers
- ❑ Lesions on limbs

February 1996

Calcitonin
Congenital adrenal hyperplasia
Chromophobe adenoma
Hypoglycaemia in diabetes
SIADH
Infertility and amenorrhoea

October 1995

Elevated free thyroxine level
Acromegaly
Cushing's syndrome
The insulin resistance syndrome

July 1995

Graves' disease
Acromegaly
Raised parathyroid hormone

February 1995

Hirsutism and amenorrhoea
Vitamin D metabolism
Hypothyroidism
IDDM

October 1994

Type II diabetes
Addison's disease
Parathyroid hormone-related protein
Cushing's syndrome

July 1994

Metabolism of thyroid hormone T3
Microalbuminuria in diabetes
Cushing's syndrome
Associations of hyperprolactinaemia
Features of primary adrenal insufficiency

February 1994

Causes of hypoglycaemia
Causes of low free T4 levels
Acromegaly
Cushing's syndrome
Drugs which inhibit hepatic gluconeogenesis

October 1993

Hormones secreted by pituitary
Polycystic ovarian syndrome
Type I diabetes
Unilateral exophthalmos
Causes of abnormal ACTH release
Weight gain

July 1993

Features of insulin-induced hypoglycaemia
Polycystic ovary syndrome
Causes of excess sweating
Hypopituitarism

February 1993

Congenital adrenal hyperplasia
Papillary carcinoma of the thyroid
Physiological responses to hypoglycaemia

October 1992
- Cushing's syndrome
- Primary hyperparathyroidism

July 1992
- Short stature
- Calcitonin
- Insulinoma
- Hyperprolactinaemia
- Congenital adrenal hyperplasia

February 1992
- Inappropriate ADH secretion
- Myxoedema
- Chromophobe adenomas
- Low thyroxine levels

October 1991
- Insulin-dependent diabetes
- Serum thyroxine levels

February 1991
- Cushing's syndrome
- Thyroxine metabolism

ENDOCRINOLOGY: TOPIC FREQUENCY INDEX

Diabetes	Feb 96, Feb 95, Oct 95, Oct 94, July 94, Oct 93, Oct 91
Cushing's syndrome	Oct 95, Oct 94, July 94, Feb 94, Oct 92, Feb 91
Thyroxine	Oct 95, July 94, Feb 94 Feb 92, Oct 91, Feb 91
Hypoglycaemia	Feb 96, Feb 94, July 93, Feb 93
Acromegaly	Oct 95, July 95, Feb 94
Congenital adrenal hyperplasia	Feb 96, Feb 93, July 92
Parathyroid hormone	July 95, Oct 94, Oct 92
Addison's disease	Oct 94, July 94
Calcitonin	Feb 96, July 92
Chromophobe adenoma	Feb 96, Feb 92
Hyperprolactinaemia	July 94, July 92
Hypothyroidism	Feb 95, Feb 92
Polycystic ovarian syndrome	Oct 93, July 93
SIADH	Feb 96, Feb 92
ACTH	Oct 93
Excess sweating	July 93
Exophthalmos	Oct 93
Graves' disease	July 95
Hepatic gluconeogenesis	Feb 94
Hirsutism	Feb 95
Hypopituitarism	July 93
Infertility	Feb 96
Insulinoma	July 92
Papillary carcinoma of the thyroid	Feb 93
Pituitary hormones	Oct 93
Short stature	July 92
Weight gain	Oct 93

ENDOCRINOLOGY: REVISION CHECKLIST

Average 4 questions per exam. Numbers in brackets indicate the relative frequency of topics.
(See also insulin, aldosterone secretion and ADH in *Basic Science* section.)

Diabetes and glycaemic control

- ❑ Diabetes (7)
- ❑ Hypoglycaemia (4)
- ❑ Hepatic gluconeogenesis
- ❑ Insulinoma

Adrenal disease

- ❑ Cushing's syndrome (6)
- ❑ Congenital adrenal hyperplasia (3)
- ❑ Addison's disease (2)
- ❑ ACTH action

Thyroid/Parathyroid disease

- ❑ Action/metabolism of thyroxine (6)
- ❑ PTH (3)
- ❑ Calcitonin (2)
- ❑ Graves' disease/exophthalmos (2)
- ❑ Hypothyroidism (2)
- ❑ Thyroid cancer

Pituitary disease

- ❑ Acromegaly (3)
- ❑ Chromophobe adenoma (2)
- ❑ Hyperprolactinaemia (2)
- ❑ Hypopituitarism
- ❑ Pituitary hormones

Miscellaneous

- ❑ SIADH (2)
- ❑ Polycystic ovary syndrome/infertility (2)
- ❑ Hirsutism
- ❑ Short stature
- ❑ Sweating
- ❑ Weight gain

February 1996

Faecal occult blood detection
Gastric acid secretion
Urinary urobilinogen
Causes of diarrhoea
Viral hepatitis
Fulminant hepatic failure
Inflammatory bowel disease

October 1995

Gastrointestinal hormones
Acute gastrointestinal haemorrhage
Features of Whipple's disease

July 1995

Gilbert's syndrome
Achalasia
Associations with dysphagia
Primary biliary cirrhosis
Painful scrotal swelling

February 1995

Cellular effects of cholera toxin
Crohn's disease
Causes of villous atrophy
Oesophageal chest pain

October 1994

Gluten-sensitive enteropathy
Associations with oesophageal tumour
Crohn's disease
Features of the gastric proton pump
Carcinoid syndrome

July 1994

Ulcerative colitis
Acute pancreatitis
Pseudomembranous colitis
Carcinoma of the stomach

February 1994

Coeliac disease
Achalasia of the cardia
Primary biliary cirrhosis

October 1993

Irritable bowel syndrome
Gastrointestinal bleeding
Inflammatory bowel disease
Causes of acute pancreatitis

July 1993

Associations of ulcerative colitis
Associations of untreated coeliac disease
Investigations of oesophageal disease
Primary biliary cirrhosis

February 1993

Irritable bowel syndrome
Acute gastroenteritis
Crohn's disease
Subphrenic abscess
Coeliac disease
Causes of conjugated hyperbilirubinaemia

October 1992

Unconjugated hyperbilirubinaemia
Achalasia of the cardia
Uses of plain abdominal X-rays
Ulcerative colitis
Malabsorption syndrome

July 1992

Chronic liver disease
Bacterial colonization of the jejenum
Gastro-oesophageal reflux
Inflammatory bowel disease

February 1992

Causes of hepatic mass
Persistent vomiting
Cirrhosis of the liver
Malabsorption
Ulcerative colitis

February 1991

Acute pancreatitis
Gilbert's syndrome
Traveller's diarrhoea

GASTROENTEROLOGY: TOPIC FREQUENCY INDEX

Coeliac disease	Oct 94, Feb 94, July 93, Feb 93
Ulcerative colitis	July 94, July 93, Oct 92, Feb 92
Achalasia of the cardia	July 95, Feb 94, Oct 92
Acute pancreatitis	July 94, Oct 93, Feb 91
Crohn's disease	Feb 95, Oct 94, Feb 93
Gastrointestinal bleeding	Feb 96, Oct 95, Oct 93
Inflammatory bowel disease	Feb 96, Oct 93, July 92
Jaundice	Feb 96, Feb 93, Oct 92
Primary biliary cirrhosis	July 95, Feb 94, July 93
Chronic liver disease	Feb 92, July 92
Diarrhoea, causes of	Feb 96, Feb 91
Gastric acid secretion	Feb 96, Oct 94
Gilbert's syndrome	July 95, Feb 91
Irritable bowel syndrome	Oct 93, Feb 93
Malabsorption syndrome	Oct 92, Feb 92
Abdominal X-rays	Oct 92
Bacterial colonization of jejunum	July 92
Carcinoid syndrome	Oct 94
Carcinoma of stomach	July 94
Cholera toxin	Feb 95
Dysphagia	July 95
Fulminant hepatic failure	Feb 96
Gastroenteritis	Feb 93
Gastrointestinal hormones	Oct 95
Gastro-oesophageal reflux	July 92
Hepatic mass	Feb 92
Oesophageal chest pain	Feb 95
Oesophageal investigations	July 93
Oesophageal tumour	Oct 94
Pseudomembranous colitis	July 94
Scrotal swelling, painful	July 95
Subphrenic abscess	Feb 93
Viral hepatitis	Feb 96
Vomiting, persistent	Feb 92
Whipple's disease	Oct 95

GASTROENTEROLOGY: REVISION CHECKLIST

Average 4 questions per exam. Numbers in brackets indicate the relative frequency of topics.

Liver disease

- ❑ Jaundice (3)
- ❑ Primary biliary cirrhosis (3)
- ❑ Chronic liver disease (2)
- ❑ Gilbert's syndrome (2)
- ❑ Hepatic mass/sub-phrenic abscess (2)

Small bowel disease/Malabsorption

- ❑ Coeliac disease (5)
- ❑ Cholera toxin/gastroenteritis (3)
- ❑ Malabsorption (2)
- ❑ Carcinoid syndrome
- ❑ Whipple's disease
  (see also 'Crohn's disease' below)

Large bowel disorders

- ❑ Ulcerative colitis/Crohn's disease (9)
- ❑ Diarrhoea (2)
- ❑ Irritable bowel syndrome (2)
- ❑ Pseudomembranous colitis

Oesophageal disease

- ❑ Achalasia (3)
- ❑ Dysphagia/oesophageal tumour (2)
- ❑ Gastro-oesophageal reflux/tests (2)
- ❑ Oesophageal chest pain

Stomach and pancreas

- ❑ Acute pancreatitis (3)
- ❑ Gastric acid secretion (2)
- ❑ Persistent vomiting
- ❑ Stomach cancer

Miscellaneous

- ❑ GI tract bleeding (3)
- ❑ Abdominal X-ray
- ❑ GI hormones
- ❑ Scrotal swelling

February 1996
X-linked dominant conditions, Klinefelter's syndrome

October 1995
Klinefelter's syndrome

July 1995
Chromosomal defects
Turner's syndrome

February 1995
Genetic anticipation

October 1994
Klinefelter's syndrome

February 1994
Autosomal recessive inheritance

February 1993
Diseases associated with abnormal karyotype

October 1992
X-linked recessive conditions

July 1992
Down's syndrome

February 1992
Klinefelter's syndrome

October 1991
Turner's syndrome, Autosomal recessive conditions

February 1991
Abnormal karyotype

GENETICS: TOPIC FREQUENCY INDEX

Klinefelter's syndrome	Feb 96, Oct 95, Oct 94, Feb 92
Abnormal karyotype	Feb 93, Feb 91
Autosomal recessive conditions	Feb 94, Oct 91
Turner's syndrome	July 95, Oct 91
Chromosomal defects	July 95
Down's syndrome	July 92
Genetic anticipation	Feb 95
X-linked dominant conditions	Feb 96
X-linked recessive conditions	Oct 92

GENETICS: REVISION CHECKLIST

Average 1 question every exam. Numbers in brackets indicate the relative frequency of topics.

Syndromes

- ❑ Klinefelter's syndrome (4)
- ❑ Turner's syndrome (2)
- ❑ Down's syndrome

Modes of inheritance

- ❑ Autosomal recessive (2)
- ❑ X-linked conditions (2)
- ❑ Genetic anticipation

Miscellaneous

- ❑ Chromosomal defects
- ❑ Abnormal karyotype

February 1996

Reticulocytosis
Haemolytic anaemia in an African
Prolonged bleeding time
Iron therapy for microcytic anaemia

October 1995

Iron storage compounds
Causes of pancytopenia/splenomegaly
Causes of thrombocytosis
Causes of basophilia
Usefulness of bone marrow trephine
Drug causes of methaemoglobinaemia

July 1995

Causes of hyposplenism
Haemoglobinopathies
Folate deficiency
Uses of fresh frozen plasma infusion
Von Willebrand's disease

February 1995

Reduced red cell folate
Intravascular haemolysis
Sideroblastic anaemia

October 1994

Hodgkin's disease
Leukaemia
Haemophilia A
Causes of thrombocytopenia

July 1994

Sickle cell disease
Hereditary spherocytosis
Haemolytic anaemia
Haematological causes of splenic enlargement
Haematological causes of hyperuricaemia
Hodgkin's lymphoma

February 1994

Differentiation of Hodgkin's/non-Hodgkin's lymphoma
Sideroblastic anaemia
Sickle cell disease
Associations of haemolytic anaemia
Iron metabolism

October 1993

Abnormal haem biosynthesis
Haematological abnormalities after splenectomy
Hodgkin's disease
Auto-immune thrombocytopenia

July 1993

Polycythaemia rubra vera
Hereditary spherocytosis
Prognosis in haematological diseases
Causes of neutropenia

February 1993

Investigation of anaemia
Thalassaemia major
Hodgkin's disease
Pancytopenia and splenomegaly

October 1992

ABO blood transfusion incompatibility
Anaemia and splenomegaly
Thrombocytosis
Haemolytic anaemia

July 1992

Acute lymphoblastic leukaemia
Haemophilia A
Bone infarction in haematological disease
Basophilia
Causes of a high reticulocyte count

February 1992

Haemolytic-uraemic syndrome
Causes of macrocytosis
Iron deficiency anaemia
Methaemoglobinaemia

October 1991

Folate deficiency
Pancytopenia
Iron treatment

February 1991

Red cell fragmentation
Pernicious anaemia
Eosinophilia
Therapeutic splenectomy

HAEMATOLOGY: TOPIC FREQUENCY INDEX

Haemolytic anaemia	Feb 96, July 94, Feb 94, Oct 92, Feb 91
Hodgkin's/non-Hodgkin's lymphoma	Oct 94, July 94, Feb 94, Oct 93, Feb 93
Pancytopenia/splenomegaly	Oct 95, July 94, Feb 93, Oct 92, Oct 91
Iron metabolism/treatment	Oct 95, Feb 94, Feb 92, Oct 91
Sickle cell disease/haemoglobinopathy	July 95, July 94, Feb 94, Feb 93
Basophilia	Oct 95, July 92
Folate deficiency	July 95, Oct 91
Haemophilia	Oct 94, July 92
Hereditary spherocytosis	July 94, July 93
Leukaemia	Oct 94, July 92
Methaemoglobinaemia	Oct 95, Feb 92
Reticulocytosis	Feb 96, July 92
Sideroblastic anaemia	Feb 95, Feb 94
Splenectomy	Oct 93, Feb 91
Thrombocytopenia	Oct 94, Oct 93
Thrombocytosis	Oct 95, Oct 92
ABO blood transfusion incompatibility	Oct 92
Anaemia, investigation of	Feb 93
Bleeding time, prolonged	Feb 96
Bone infarction in haematological disease	July 92
Bone marrow trepine	Oct 95
Eosinophilia	Feb 91
Fresh frozen plasma, uses of	July 95
Haematological diseases, prognosis in	July 93
Haem biosynthesis, abnormal	Oct 93
Haemolytic-uraemic syndrome	Feb 92
Hyperuricaemia	July 94

Haematology

Hyposplenism	July 95
Intravascular haemolysis	Feb 95
Macrocytosis	Feb 92
Neutropenia	July 93
Pernicious anaemia	Feb 91
Polycythaemia rubra vera	July 93
Von Willebrand's disease	July 95

HAEMATOLOGY: REVISION CHECKLIST

Average 4 questions per exam. Numbers in brackets indicate the relative frequency of topics.

Metabolic anaemias

- ❑ Iron deficiency/metabolism/therapy (4)
- ❑ Folate deficiency (3)
- ❑ Basophilia (2)
- ❑ Macrocytosis/pernicious anaemia (2)
- ❑ Sideroblastic anaemia (2)
- ❑ Haem biosynthesis
- ❑ Investigation of anaemia

Haemolytic anaemia

- ❑ Haemolytic anaemia (5)
- ❑ Sickle cell/Haemoglobinopathy (4)
- ❑ Reticulocytosis (2)
- ❑ Haemolytic-uraemic syndrome
- ❑ Hereditary spherocytosis
- ❑ Intravascular haemolysis

Bleeding disorders

- ❑ Haemophilia (2)
- ❑ Thrombocytopaenia (2)
- ❑ Bleeding time
- ❑ Fresh frozen plasma
- ❑ Von Willebrand's disease

Haematological malignancy

- ❑ Hodgkin's/Non-Hodgkin's lymphoma (5)
- ❑ Pancytopaenia/splenomegaly (5)
- ❑ Leukaemia (2)
- ❑ Polycythaemia

Miscellaneous

- ❑ Methaemoglobinaemia (2)
- ❑ Thrombocytosis (2)
- ❑ Bone infarction
- ❑ Bone marrow test
- ❑ Eosinophilia
- ❑ Hyperuricaemia and haematological disease (see also *Metabolic Disease*)
- ❑ Hyposplenism
- ❑ Neutropaenia

February 1996

T cell deficiency
Pathogenic role of complement

October 1995

Tissue receptor antibodies and disease
Autoimmune disease
Tumour necrosis factor

July 1995

Gamma interferon
IgE and associated disease
Immunology of transplant rejection

February 1995

ANCA
Monoclonal gammopathy
Septicaemia after splenectomy

October 1994

T lymphocytes

July 1994

Interferon
IgA
Leucotrienes
Circulating immune complexes

February 1994

Hereditary angioneurotic oedema
Tumour necrosis factor
Monoclonal antibodies

October 1993

Inflammatory allergic reactions

July 1993

Angio-neurotic oedema
Deficiencies in cell-mediated immunity

October 1992

T lymphocytes
Type III hypersensitivity reactions

July 1992

Causes of low serum IgG
Specific tissue receptor antibodies

October 1991

Causes of a low CH50
Primary hypogammaglobulinaemia

February 1991

Precipitating antibodies in diagnosis

IMMUNOLOGY: TOPIC FREQUENCY INDEX

Angioneurotic oedema	Feb 94, July 93
Hypersensitivity reactions	Oct 93, Oct 92
Interferon	July 95, July 94
Monoclonal gammopathy/ antibodies	Feb 95, Feb 94
Tissue receptor antibodies	Oct 95, July 92
T lymphocytes	Oct 94, Oct 92
Tumour necrosis factor	Oct 95, Feb 94
ANCA	Feb 95
Autoimmune disease	Oct 95
CH50	Oct 91
Circulating immune complexes	July 94
Hypogammaglobulinaemia	Oct 91
IgA	July 94
IgE	July 95
IgG	July 92
Immunity, cell-mediated	July 93
Leucotrienes	July 94
Pathogenic role of complement	Feb 96
Precipitating antibodies in diagnosis	Feb 91
Septicaemia after splenectomy	Feb 95
T cell deficiency	Feb 96
Transplant rejection	July 95

IMMUNOLOGY: REVISION CHECKLIST

Coverage of immunology in the exam is increasing, with an average 2–3 questions per exam during the last 3 years. Numbers in brackets indicate the relative frequency of topics.

Cellular immunity

- ❑ T lymphocytes/deficiency (3)
- ❑ Cell-mediated immunity

Cytokines

- ❑ Interferon (2)
- ❑ Tumour necrosis factor (2)
- ❑ Leukotrienes

Immunoglobulins/autoimmunity

- ❑ IgA/IgE/IgG (3)
- ❑ Autoimmune disease/ANCA (2)
- ❑ Monoclonal gammopathy (2)
- ❑ Tissue receptor antibodies (2)
- ❑ Circulating immune complexes
- ❑ Hypogammaglobulinaemia
- ❑ Precipitating antibodies in diagnosis

Miscellaneous

- ❑ Angioneurotic oedema (2)
- ❑ Complement/CH50 (2)
- ❑ Hypersensitivity reactions (2)
- ❑ Post-splenectomy
- ❑ Transplant rejection

February 1996

Adenovirus infection
Pneumonia
Malaria
Rubella
Chlamydia trachomatis

October 1995

Features of staphylococcal toxins
Infectious mononucleosis
Brucellosis
Infections causing diarrhoea
Toxoplasmosis

July 1995

Malaria
Parvovirus B19
Genital herpes

February 1995

Non-gonococcal urethritis
Chickenpox
Tuberculosis
Malaria
Hepatitis E

October 1994

Acute hepatitis B
Pneumocystis carinii
Malaria
Tetanus

July 1994

Infectious mononucleosis
Infections that cause eosinophilia
Giardia lamblia infection
Falciparum malaria
Brucellosis/Toxoplasmosis

February 1994

Hepatitis C
Features of rubella
Helicobacter pylori
Human prion disease
Chronic brucellosis

October 1993

Associations of HIV infection
Tropical fever and splenomegaly
Non-gonococcal urethritis
BCG immunization

July 1993

Lyme disease
Toxoplasmosis
Mumps
Infection with *Neisseria gonorrhoea*
Infectious mononucleosis
Causes of neurological disease in AIDS patients

February 1993

Cholera
Tetanus
Syphilis

October 1992

Brucellosis
Shistosomiasis
Measles encephalitis
AIDS

July 1992

Causes of rash, lymphadenopathy and fever
Infectious diarrhoea
Tuberculosis
Plasmodium malariae

February 1992

Rubella
Falciparum malaria

October 1991

Tuberculosis
Typhoid
Faecal oral transmission
Giardiasis
Chlamydia trachomatis
Hepatitis B infection

February 1991

Infectious mononucleosis
Transmission by insect bite

Malaria	Feb 96, July 95, Feb 95, Oct 94, July 94, July 92, Feb 92
Brucellosis	Oct 95, July 94, Feb 94, Oct 92
Hepatitis	Feb 95, Oct 94, Feb 94, Oct 91
Infectious mononucleosis	Oct 95, July 94, July 93, Feb 91
AIDS/HIV	Oct 93, July 93, Oct 92
Rubella	Feb 96, Feb 94, Feb 92
Toxoplasmosis	Oct 95, July 94, July 93
Tuberculosis	Feb 95, July 92, Oct 91
Chlamydia	Feb 96, Oct 91
Infections causing diarrhoea	Oct 95, July 92
Non-gonococcal urethritis	Feb 95, Oct 93
Tetanus	Oct 94, Feb 93
Adenovirus infection	Feb 96
BCG imunization	Oct 93
Chickenpox	Feb 95
Cholera	Feb 93
Faecal-oral transmission	Oct 91
Genital herpes	July 95
Helicobacter pylori	Feb 94
Human prion disease	Feb 94
Infections causing eosinophilia	July 94
Lyme disease	July 93
Measles	Oct 92
Mumps	July 93
Neisseria gonorrhoea	July 93
Parvovirus B19	July 95
Pneumocystis carinii	Oct 94
Pneumonia	Feb 96

Rash, lympadenopathy and fever, causes of	July 92
Shistosomiasis	Oct 92
Staphylococcus	Oct 95
Syphilis	Feb 93
Transmission by insect bite	Oct 91
Tropical fever and splenomegaly	Oct 93
Typhoid	Oct 91

INFECTIOUS DISEASES: REVISION CHECKLIST

Average 4 questions per exam. Numbers in brackets indicate the relative frequency of topics.

Viral Infections

- ❑ Hepatitis (4)
- ❑ AIDS/HIV (3)
- ❑ Chickenpox/measles/mumps (3)
- ❑ Adenovirus
- ❑ Genital herpes
- ❑ Parvovirus

Bacterial Infections

- ❑ Venereal disease (5)
- ❑ Infectious mononucleosis (4)
- ❑ Brucellosis (4)
- ❑ TB/BCG (4)
- ❑ Toxoplasmosis (3)
- ❑ Tetanus (2)
- ❑ Typhoid/cholera (2)
- ❑ *Helicobacter pylori*
- ❑ Pneumonia
- ❑ *Staphylococcus*

Routes of infection

- ❑ Faecal-oral transmission
- ❑ Transmission by insect bite

Tropical and protozoal infections

- ❑ Malaria (7)
- ❑ Tropical fever/splenomegaly (2)
- ❑ *Pneumocystis carinii*
- ❑ Schistosomiasis

Miscellaneous

- ❑ *Chlamydia trachomatis* (2)
- ❑ Other infections/diarrhoea (2)
- ❑ Infections and eosinophilia
- ❑ Lyme disease
- ❑ Prion disease

February 1996

Carbon monoxide poisoning
Excessive alcohol intake

October 1995

Causes of hypomagnesaemia
Malignant-neuroleptic syndrome
Wilson's disease

July 1995

Salicylate poisoning
Hypokalaemic acidosis
Homocystinuria
Causes of hyponatraemia

February 1995

Persistent vomiting
Hypomagnesaemia
Paget's disease
Tricyclic overdose
Hypophosphataemia
Vitamin D metabolism

October 1994

Overdose of paracetamol

July 1994

Metabolism of vitamin D
Iron toxicity
Chloride depletion
Hypothermia

February 1994

Causes of hypercalcaemia

October 1993

Raised alkaline phosphatase
Acute poisoning

July 1993

Features of theophylline overdose
Hypokalaemic acidosis
Kwashiorkor
Causes of hyperuricaemia

February 1993

Achondroplasia
Hypophosphataemic rickets
Causes of hypokalaemia
Osteoporosis

October 1992

Osteoporosis
Hypercarotinaemia

July 1992

Causes of hypomagnesaemia
Accidental hypothermia
Paracetamol poisoning

February 1992

Effects of heavy alcohol intake
Osteoporosis
Familial hypercholesterolaemia
Causes of alkalosis
Obesity
Overdose of drugs

October 1991

Polydypsia
Wilson's disease

February 1991

Familial hypercholesterolaemia
$Alpha_1$-antitrypsin deficiency
Hyperkalaemic acidosis
Thiamine deficiency

METABOLIC DISEASE: TOPIC FREQUENCY INDEX

Overdose/poisoning	Feb 96, July 95, Feb 95, Oct 94, July 94, Oct 93, July 93, Oct 92, July 92
Hypokalaemia	July 95, July 93, Feb 93
Hypomagnesaemia	Oct 95, Feb 95, July 92
Osteoporosis	Feb 93, Oct 92, Feb 92
Alcohol intake, excessive	Feb 96, Feb 92
Hypercholesterolaemia, familial	Feb 92, Feb 91
Hypophosphataemia	Feb 95, Feb 93
Hypothermia	July 94, July 92
Vitamin D metabolism	Feb 95, July 94
Wilson's disease	Oct 95, Oct 91
Achondroplasia	Feb 93
Alkaline phosphatase, raised	Oct 93
Alkalosis, causes of	Feb 92
$Alpha_1$-antitrypsin deficiency	Feb 91
Chloride depletion	July 94
Homocystinuria	July 95
Hypercalcaemia	Feb 94
Hypercarotinaemia	Oct 92
Hyperkalaemia	Feb 91
Hyperuricaemia	July 93
Hyponatraemia	July 95
Kwashiorkor	July 93
Malignant-neuroleptic syndrome	Oct 95
Obesity	Feb 92
Paget's disease	Feb 95
Polydipsia	Oct 91
Thiamine deficiency	Feb 91
Vomiting, persistent	Feb 95

METABOLIC DISEASE: REVISION CHECKLIST

Average 3 questions per exam. Numbers in brackets indicate the relative frequency of topics.

Overdose and poisoning

- ❑ Carbon monoxide/other poisoning (3)
- ❑ Salicylate/paracetamol overdose (3)
- ❑ Excess alcohol (2)
- ❑ Tricyclic/theophylline overdose (2)
- ❑ Iron toxicity

Disorders of bone

- ❑ Osteoporosis (3)
- ❑ Vitamin D metabolism (2)
- ❑ Achondroplasia
- ❑ Increased alkaline phosphatase
- ❑ Paget's disease

Disorders of acid/base and electrolytes

- ❑ Hyper/hypokalaemia (4)
- ❑ Hypomagnesaemia (3)
- ❑ Alkalosis/vomiting (2)
- ❑ Hyponatraemia/chloride depletion (2)
- ❑ Hypophosphataemia (2)
- ❑ Hypercalcaemia
- ❑ Polydipsia

Inherited metabolic disorders

- ❑ Hypercholesterolaemia (2)
- ❑ Wilson's disease (2)
- ❑ $Alpha_1$-antitrypsin deficiency *(see also Basic Science)*
- ❑ Homocystinuria
- ❑ Malignant neuroleptic syndrome

Miscellaneous

- ❑ Hypothermia (2)
- ❑ Hypercarotenemia
- ❑ Hyperuricaemia
- ❑ Kwashiorkor
- ❑ Obesity
- ❑ Thiamine deficiency

NEPHROLOGY: EXAM TOPICS

February 1996

Normal renal tubular function
Polycystic kidney disease
Hypocomplementaemia and glomerulonephritis
Minimal change disease

October 1995

Distal renal tubular acidosis
Renal vein thrombosis
Membranous nephropathy
Microalbuminuria in diabetes

July 1995

ARF and rhabdomyolysis
Macroscopic haematuria
Renal papillary necrosis

February 1995

Acute or chronic renal failure
Polycystic kidney disease
Nephrotic syndrome
Membranous glomerulonephritis

October 1994

Distal renal tubular acidosis
Nephrotic syndrome
Differentiation of acute and chronic renal failure
Hypertension and chronic renal failure

July 1994

Minimal change nephropathy
Factors affecting urine concentration
Chronic renal failure
Analgesic nephropathy

February 1994

Acute renal failure resulting from overdose
Adult polycystic kidney disease
Aetiology of chronic renal failure
Nephrotic range proteinuria
Uraemic osteodystrophy
Physiology of the proximal renal tubule

October 1993

Nephrotic syndrome
Diabetic microalbuminuria
Renal vein thrombosis
Normal renal tubular physiology

July 1993

Distal renal tubular acidosis
Nephrotic syndrome

February 1993

Renal water excretion
Haemolytic-uraemic syndrome

October 1992

Discolouration of the urine
Causes of nocturia
Lupus nephritis
Minimal change nephrotic syndrome

July 1992

Renal papillary necrosis
Nephrotic range proteinuria
Causes of acute on chronic renal failure

February 1992

Causes of polyuria
Membranous glomerulonephritis

October 1991

Acute renal failure and rhabdomyolysis
Nephrotic syndrome

February 1991

Macroscopic haematuria
Papillary necrosis
Membranous glomerulonephritis
Haemolytic uraemic syndrome
Drugs in renal failure

NEPHROLOGY: TOPIC FREQUENCY INDEX

Nephrotic syndrome	Feb 95, Oct 94, Feb 94, Oct 93, July 93, July 92, Oct 91
Membranous glomerulonephritis	Oct 95, Feb 95, Feb 92, Feb 91
Distal renal tubular acidosis	Oct 95, Oct 94, July 93
Minimal change nephropathy	Feb 96, July 94, Oct 92
Polycystic kidney disease	Feb 96, Feb 95, Feb 94
Renal failure, acute vs chronic	Feb 95, Oct 94, July 92
Renal failure, chronic	Oct 94, July 94, Feb 94
Renal papillary necrosis	July 95, July 92, Feb 91
Renal physiology/function, normal	Feb 96, Feb 94, Oct 93
Acute RF and overdose	Feb 94, Feb 91
Acute RF and rhabdomyolysis	July 95, Oct 91
Diabetic microalbuminuria	Oct 95, Oct 93
Haemolytic-uraemic syndrome	Feb 93, Feb 91
Macroscopic haematuria	July 95, Feb 91
Renal vein thrombosis	Oct 95, Oct 93
Water excretion/urine concentration	July 94, Feb 93
Analgesic nephropathy	July 94
Hypocomplementaemia and GN	Feb 96
Lupus nephritis	Oct 92
Nocturia	Oct 92
Polyuria	Feb 92
Uraemic osteodystrophy	Feb 94
Urine discolouration	Oct 92

NEPHROLOGY: REVISION CHECKLIST

Average 3–4 questions per exam. Numbers in brackets indicate the relative frequency of topics.

Nephrotic syndrome/related glomerulonephritis

- ❑ Nephrotic syndrome (7)
- ❑ Membranous glomerulonephritis (4)
- ❑ Minimal Change disease (3)
- ❑ Renal vein thrombosis (2)
- ❑ Hypocomplementaemia & glomerulonephritis
- ❑ SLE nephritis

Renal failure

- ❑ Acute versus chronic (3)
- ❑ Chronic renal failure (3)
- ❑ Acute renal failure (2)
- ❑ Haemolytic-uraemic syndrome (2)
- ❑ Rhabdomyolysis (2)

Urinary abnormalities

- ❑ Macroscopic haematuria (2)
- ❑ Discolouration of the urine
- ❑ Nocturia
- ❑ Polyuria

Basic renal physiology

- ❑ Normal renal physiology/function (3)
- ❑ Water excretion/urinary concentration (2)

Miscellaneous

- ❑ Distal renal tubular acidosis (3)
- ❑ Renal papillary necrosis (3)
- ❑ Diabetic nephropathy (2)
- ❑ Analgesic nephropathy
- ❑ Renal osteodystrophy

February 1996

Lesion of 7th cranial nerve
Posterior interosseous nerve
Temporal lobe epilepsy
Paraesthesia
Duchenne muscular dystrophy
Multiple sclerosis

October 1995

Median nerve lesion
Section of posterior nerve roots
Normal pressure hydrocephalus
Guillan-Barré syndrome
Parkinson's disease

July 1995

Pyramidal tracts
Down-beat nystagmus
Radial nerve in upper arm
Cerebral circulatory disorders
Encephalitis
Central pontine myelinolysis
Prognosis of head injury

February 1995

Drug causes of dyskinesia
Finger weakness
Lesion of pre-frontal cortex
Lumbar puncture
Dementia
Vertigo

October 1994

Hemiplegic migraine
Cerebral control of finger movements
Causes of cerebral abscess
CNS involvement in AIDS
Complete third nerve palsy
Causes of ataxia
Autonomic neuropathy
Features of cervical spondylosis

July 1994

Features of a parietal lobe lesion
Lesion of the sixth cranial nerve
Anatomical pathways for the pupillary light reflex
Duchenne muscular dystrophy
Causes of truncal ataxia
Causes of intracranial calcification

February 1994

Internuclear ophthalmoplegia
Prognostic indicators in multiple sclerosis
Prognosis of head injury
Dementia
Features of myotonic dystrophy
Neurological tracts within the spinal cord

October 1993

Duchenne muscular dystrophy
Superior oblique muscle palsy
Lateral medullary syndrome
Innervation of the muscles of the hand
Transient ischaemic attacks

July 1993

Lesion of the sciatic nerve
Causes of down-beat nystagmus
Neurological prognosis after head injury

February 1993

Causes of muscle fasciculation
Chronic subdural haematoma
Dystrophia myotonica
Lesion of the facial nerve
Cranial nerves carrying parasympathetic fibres
Benign intracranial hypertension
Occlusion of the posterior cerebral artery

October 1992

Section of the dorsal interosseus nerve
Pseudo-fits
Multiple sclerosis
Guillain-Barré syndrome
Bulbar palsy
Temporal lobe epilepsy

July 1992

Facial nerve lesion
Headache
Nerve root innervation of muscles
Cranial nerve lesions
Brain tumour

February 1992

Duchenne muscular dystrophy
Section of the posterior nerve roots
Causes of nystagmus
Migraine
CSF lymphocytosis
Alzheimer's disease
Recent memory loss
Seventh cranial nerve

October 1991

Transection of the facial nerve
Benign essential tremor
Lesions of the posterior spinal ganglia

February 1991

Dysarthria
Alzheimer's disease
Combined upper/lower motor neurone lesion
Damage to the median nerve
EEG abnormalities

NEUROLOGY: TOPIC FREQUENCY INDEX

Duchenne muscular dystrophy	Feb 96, July 94, Oct 93, Feb 92
Facial nerve	Feb 96, Feb 93, July 92, Oct 91
Cranial nerve lesions (various)	July 94, July 92, Feb 92
Down-beat nystagmus	July 95, July 93, Feb 92
Head injury, prognosis of	July 95, Feb 94, July 93
Multiple sclerosis	Feb 96, Feb 94, Oct 92
Nerve root innervation of muscles	Feb 95, Oct 93, July 92
Posterior nerve roots, section of	Oct 95, Feb 92, Oct 91
Alzheimer's disease	Feb 92, Feb 91
Ataxia	Oct 94, July 94
Dementia	Feb 95, Feb 94
Dorsal interosseus nerve	Feb 96, Oct 92
Guillain-Barré syndrome	Oct 95, Oct 92
Hemiplegic migraine	Oct 94, Feb 92
Median nerve lesion	Oct 95, Feb 91
Myotonic dystrophy	Feb 94, Feb 93
Temporal lobe epilepsy	Feb 96, Oct 92
AIDS, CNS involvement in	Oct 94
Autonomic neuropathy	Oct 94
Benign essential tremor	Oct 91
Benign intracranial hypertension	Feb 93
Brain tumour	July 92
Bulbar palsy	Oct 92
Central pontine myelinolysis	July 95
Cerebral abscess, causes of	Oct 94
Cerebral circulatory disorders	July 95
Cervical spondylitis	Oct 94
Cranial nerves carrying parasympathetic fibres	Feb 93
CSF lymphocytosis	Feb 92

Dysarthria	Feb 91
Dyskinesia	Feb 95
EEG abnormalities	Feb 91
Encephalitis	July 95
Finger movements, cerebral control of	Oct 94
Headache	July 92
Internuclear ophthalmoplegia	Feb 94
Intracranial calcification	July 94
Lateral medullary syndrome	Oct 93
Lumbar puncture	Feb 95
Memory loss	Feb 92
Motor neurone lesion, combined upper/lower	Feb 91
Muscle fasciculation	Feb 93
Normal pressure hydrocephalus	Oct 95
Paraesthesia	Feb 96
Parietal lobe lesion	July 94
Parkinson's disease	Oct 95
Posterior cerebral artery, occlusion of	Feb 93
Pre-frontal cortex, lesion of	Feb 95
Pseudo-fits	Oct 92
Pupillary light reflex	July 94
Pyramidal tracts	July 95
Radial nerve	July 95
Sciatic nerve lesion	July 93
Spinal cord	Feb 94
Subdural haematoma	Feb 93
Superior oblique muscle palsy	Oct 93
Third nerve palsy	Oct 94
Transient ischaemic attacks	Oct 93
Vertigo	Feb 95

NEUROLOGY: REVISION CHECKLIST

Average 5–6 questions per exam, including anatomy of the nervous system (excluded from Basic Sciences section). Numbers in brackets indicate the relative frequency of topics.

Abnormalities of brain & cerebral circulation

- ❑ Dementia/Alzheimer's (5)
- ❑ Lateral medullary/circulatory syndromes (3)
- ❑ Head injury (3)
- ❑ Benign intracranial hypertension/brain tumour (2)
- ❑ Hemiplegic migraine (2)
- ❑ Parietal lobe/frontal cortical lesions (2)
- ❑ Temporal lobe epilepsy (2)
- ❑ Central pontine myelinolysis
- ❑ Cerebral abscess
- ❑ EEG
- ❑ Encephalitis
- ❑ Intracranial calcification
- ❑ Normal pressure hydrocephalus
- ❑ Subdural haematoma
- ❑ Transient ischaemic attacks

Spinal cord and peripheral nerve anatomy & lesions

- ❑ Innervation of hand muscles (3)
- ❑ Posterior nerve root/spinal ganglia lesions (3)
- ❑ Dorsal interosseous nerve (2)
- ❑ Guillain-Barré (2)
- ❑ Median nerve (2)
- ❑ Cervical spondylosis
- ❑ Paraesthesia
- ❑ Pyramidal tracts
- ❑ Radial nerve
- ❑ Sciatic nerve lesion
- ❑ Spinal cord lesions

Cranial nerve anatomy & lesions

- ❑ Cranial nerve lesions (3)
- ❑ Facial nerve (4)
- ❑ Third nerve palsy/pupillary reflex (2)
- ❑ Bulbar palsy
- ❑ Internuclear ophthalmoplegia
- ❑ 4th nerve palsy

Dyskinesias

- ❑ Ataxia (2)
- ❑ Benign essential tremor
- ❑ Dyskinesia
- ❑ Parkinson's disease

Muscular disorders

- ❑ Duchenne muscular dystrophy (4)
- ❑ Myotonic dystrophy (2)

Miscellaneous

- ❑ Multiple sclerosis (3)
- ❑ Nystagmus (3)
- ❑ Lumbar puncture/CSF (2)
- ❑ Vertigo/dysarthria (2)
- ❑ Autonomic neuropathy
- ❑ CNS involvement in AIDS
- ❑ Headache
- ❑ Pseudofits

July 1995
Diabetic retinopathy

February 1995
Central retinal vein occlusion

October 1993
Background diabetic retinopathy

February 1993
Uveitis

October 1992
Causes of painful ophthalmoplegia

July 1992
Central scotoma

February 1992
Diabetic eye changes

October 1991
Cataracts

February 1991
Papilloedema

OPHTHALMOLOGY: TOPIC FREQUENCY INDEX

Diabetic eye changes	July 95, Oct 93, Feb 92
Cataracts	Oct 91
Central retinal vein occlusion	Feb 95
Central scotoma	July 92
Painful ophthalmoplegia	Oct 92
Papilloedema	Feb 91
Uveitis	Feb 93

OPHTHALMOLOGY: REVISION CHECKLIST

Average 1 question every 2 examinations. Numbers in brackets indicate the relative frequency of topics.

Retinal and optic disc disease

❑ Diabetic eye changes (3)
❑ Central retinal vein occlusion
❑ Papilloedema

Visual field defects

❑ Central scotoma

Miscellaneous

❑ Cataracts
❑ Painful ophthalmoplegia
❑ Uveitis

February 1996

Drugs in breast-feeding mothers
Drugs causing hypothyroidism
Adverse reactions from combination drugs
Adverse effects of thiazides

October 1995

Drugs which exacerbate asthma
Adverse effects of drugs
Drugs which interact with warfarin

July 1995

Contraindications for ACE inhibition
Mechanisms of drug action
Atenolol
Drugs and increase in digoxin level
HMG CoA-reductase inhibitors

February 1995

Amiodarone
Drug interactions
Azidothymidine (AZT)
Dosage reduction in renal failure

October 1994

Sumatriptan
Etidronate
Selective $alpha_1$ blockade

July 1994

Sodium valproate
Oral iron therapy
Drugs enhancing the action of dopamine
Toxic effects of amiodarone
Side-effects of thiazides

February 1994

Sulphasalazine
L-dopa
Terminal care pain control with morphine
Effects of lithium
Gentamicin therapy
Effects of anti-convulsants
Drugs requiring dosage reduction in renal failure
Radio-iodine treatment

October 1993

Interactions between drugs and the contraceptive pill
Drugs and adverse effects
ACE inhibitors
Non-steroidal anti-inflammatory agents
Side-effects of sulphasalazine

July 1993

Enzyme inducers
Side-effects of isoretinoin
Penicillamine
Metronidazole

February 1993

Cimetidine
Digoxin overdose
Drugs and acute intermittent porphyria

October 1992

Enalapril
Hypokalaemic side-effects of drug therapy
Serious drug interactions
Drug induced hypothyroidism

July 1992

Griseofulvin
Mechanisms of antibiotic action
Chlorpromazine
Amitriptyline

February 1992

Drugs causing gynaecomastia
Hazardous drug combinations
Cisplatinum side-effects
Drugs crossing the placenta
Oral hypoglycaemics

October 1991

Interactions with warfarin
Unwanted effects of digoxin
Thiazide diuretics
Unwanted effects of drugs
Drugs causing convulsions

February 1991

Amiodarone
Carbimazole
Drugs in pregnancy
Drugs interacting with prolactin secretion
Oral contraceptive pill side-effects

PHARMACOLOGY: TOPIC FREQUENCY CHECKLIST

Drug interactions	Feb 96, Oct 95, Feb 95, July 94, Oct 93, Oct 92, Feb 92, Feb 91
ACE inhibitors	July 95, Oct 93, Oct 92
Adverse effects of drugs	Oct 95, Oct 93, Oct 91
Amiodarone	Feb 95, July 94, Feb 91
Digoxin	July 95, Feb 93, Oct 91
Drugs in renal failure	Feb 95, Feb 94, Feb 93
Thiazides	Feb 96, July 94, Oct 91
Drugs and breast-feeding	Feb 96, Feb 91
Drugs causing hypothyroidism	Feb 96, Oct 92
Drugs in pregnancy	Feb 92, Feb 91
Sulphasalazine	Feb 94, Oct 93
$Alpha_1$ blockade	Oct 94
Amitriptyline	July 92
Antibiotic action	July 92
Anticonvulsants	Feb 94
Atenolol	July 95
Azidothymidine	Feb 95
Carbimazole	Feb 91
Chlorpromazine	July 92
Cimetidine	Feb 93
Cisplatinum	Feb 92
Drugs causing convulsions	Oct 91
Drugs causing gynaecomastia	Feb 92
Drugs causing hypokalaemia	Oct 92
Drugs exacerbating asthma	Oct 95
Enzyme inducers	July 93
Etidronate	Oct 94
Gentamicin	Feb 94
Griseofulvin	July 92
HMG CoA-reductase inhibitors	July 95
Isoretinoin	July 93
L-dopa	Feb 94
Lithium	Feb 94

Pharmacology

Mechanisms of drug action	July 95
Metronidazole	July 93
NSAIDs	Oct 93
Oral hypoglycaemics	Feb 92
Oral iron therapy	July 94 *(see also Haematology)*
Pain control	Feb 94
Penicillamine	July 93
Radio-iodine	Feb 94
Sodium valproate	July 94
Sumatriptan	Oct 94
Warfarin	Oct 91

Average 4–5 questions per exam. Numbers in brackets indicate the relative frequency of topics.

Interactions/dose adjustment

- ❑ Drug interactions (8)
- ❑ Pregnancy/breast feeding (4)
- ❑ Dose adjustment in renal failure (3)
- ❑ Adverse effects – general (3)

Specific side-effects of drugs

- ❑ Causing hypothyroidism (2)
- ❑ Asthma exacerbation
- ❑ Convulsions
- ❑ Gynaecomastia
- ❑ Hepatic enzyme inducers
- ❑ Hypokalaemia

Fundamental pharmacology

- ❑ Mechanisms of drug/antibiotic action (2)

Most frequently considered individual agents

- ❑ Antipsychotics/depressants (4)
- ❑ ACE inhibitors (3)
- ❑ Amiodarone (3)
- ❑ Digoxin (3)
- ❑ Thiazides (3)
- ❑ Anti-convulsants (2)
- ❑ Sulphasalazine (2)

Other 'topical' agents

- ❑ Azidothymidine (AZT)
- ❑ Gentamicin
- ❑ HMG Co-A reductase inhibitor
- ❑ L-dopa
- ❑ Lithium
- ❑ Penicillamine
- ❑ Warfarin

PSYCHIATRY: EXAM TOPICS

February 1996

Anorexia nervosa
Dementia/depression
Somatization syndrome
Schizophrenia

October 1995

Bulimia nervosa
Obsessional neurosis
Insomnia
Features of mania

July 1995

Anorexia nervosa
Depression in the elderly
Mania
Acute confusional state

February 1995

Depression
Schizophrenia
Anorexia nervosa
Narcolepsy

October 1994

Causes of visual hallucinations
Acute mania
Features of delirium tremens
Emotional lability

July 1994

Schizophrenia
Dementia
Neurosis
Psychogenic symptoms

February 1994

Risk of successful suicide
Features of obsessive-compulsive disorders
Features suggesting an organic basis for psychiatric symptoms

October 1993

Adult alcohol dependency syndrome
Paranoid delusions
Neuropsychiatric symptoms and organic disease
Causes of sleep disturbance

July 1993

Acute schizophrenia
Obsessional neurosis
Depression/dementia
Bulimia

February 1993

Endogenous depression
Obsessive-compulsive state
Mania
Schizophrenia

October 1992

Anorexia nervosa
Narcolepsy

July 1992

Conversion syndromes
Disorders of affect
Persecutory delusions
Eating disorders

February 1992

Schizophrenia

Organic psychiatric symptoms

October 1991

Anorexia nervosa

Mania

February 1991

Anxiety

Depression in the elderly

Anorexia nervosa

PSYCHIATRY: TOPIC FREQUENCY CHECKLIST

Anorexia nervosa	Feb 96, July 95, Feb 95, Oct 92, July 92, Oct 91, Feb 91
Schizophrenia	Feb 96, Feb 95, July 94, July 93, Feb 93, Feb 92
Mania	Oct 95, July 95, Oct 94, Feb 93, Oct 91
Depression	July 95, Feb 95, Feb 93, Feb 91
Organic disease	Feb 94, Oct 93, Feb 92
Alcohol dependency	Oct 94, Oct 93
Bulimia nervosa	Oct 95, July 93
Depression versus dementia	Feb 96, July 93
Insomnia	Oct 95, Oct 93
Narcolepsy	Feb 95, Oct 92
Obsessional neurosis	Oct 95, July 93
Obsessive-compulsive disorders	Feb 94, Feb 93
Acute confusional state	July 95
Anxiety	Feb 91
Conversion syndromes	July 92
Delusions, paranoid	Oct 93
Delusions, persecutory	July 92
Dementia	July 94
Disorders of affect	July 92
Emotional lability	Oct 94
Hallucinations, visual	Oct 94
Neurosis	July 94
Psychogenic symptoms	July 94
Somatization syndrome	Feb 96
Suicide	Feb 94

PSYCHIATRY: REVISION CHECKLIST

Average 4 questions per exam. Numbers in brackets indicate the relative frequency of topics.

Psychotic disorders

- ❑ Depression/insomnia (6)
- ❑ Schizophrenia (6)
- ❑ Mania (5)
- ❑ Hallucinations/delusions (3)

Anxiety states/compulsive disorders

- ❑ Neurosis/psychogenic/conversion (4)
- ❑ Obsessional/compulsive disorders (4)

Eating disorders

- ❑ Anorexia nervosa (7)
- ❑ Bulimia (2)

Other cognitive disorders

- ❑ Dementia (3)
- ❑ Acute confusional state

Miscellaneous

- ❑ Alcohol dependency (2)
- ❑ Narcolepsy (2)

February 1996

Sleep apnoea syndrome
Pulmonary complications of SLE
Pulmonary aspergillosis
Pneumothorax

October 1995

Bronchopulmonary aspergillosis
Bronchial carcinoid tumour
Extrinsic allergic alveolitis
Mycoplasma pneumoniae

July 1995

Adult respiratory distress syndrome
Exercise-induced asthma
Obstructive sleep apnoea

February 1995

Community-acquired pneumonia
Oat cell bronchial carcinoma
Pulmonary eosinophilia

October 1994

Type I respiratory failure
Causes of calcification on chest X-ray
Bullous emphysema
Pulmonary manifestation of SLE

July 1994

Transfer factor
Lung perfusion scanning
Indications for long-term oxygen therapy
Community acquired pneumonia

February 1994

Causes of pulmonary cavitation
Emphysema
Small cell carcinoma of the lung

October 1993

Causes of respiratory failure
Sarcoidosis
The transfer factor
Causes of respiratory crackles on auscultation
Bronchiectasis

July 1993

Fibrosing alveolitis
Predisposition to bronchial carcinoma
Normal pulmonary physiology

February 1993

Pulmonary aspergillosis
Severe asthma attack
Causes of bronchiectasis

October 1992

Acute bronchiolitis
Adult respiratory distress syndrome
Lung function tests
Obstructive sleep apnoea
Occupational asthma
Physiological characteristics of normal ventilation

July 1992

Pancoast's tumour of lung
Asbestosis
Sarcoidosis
Abnormalities of chest X-ray

February 1992

Respiratory distress syndrome
Extrinsic allergic alveolitis
Atypical pneumonias
Surgery for lung cancer
Aetiology of chronic respiratory disease

October 1991

Mycoplasma pneumoniae
Respiratory manifestations of rheumatoid arthritis
Clubbing
Type II respiratory failure
Psittacosis
Bronchial carcinoid syndrome
Extrinsic allergic alveolitis

February 1991

Viral respiratory infections
Spontaneous pneumothorax
Alveolar hyperventilation
Farmer's lung
Obstructive sleep apnoea

Topic	Frequency
Pneumonia	Oct 95, Feb 95, July 94, Feb 92, Oct 91
Bronchial carcinoma	Oct 95, Feb 95, July 93, Oct 91
Sleep apnoea syndrome	Feb 96, July 95, Oct 92, Feb 91
Asthma	July 95, Feb 93, Oct 92
Extrinsic allergic alveolitis	Oct 95, Feb 92, Oct 91
Pulmonary aspergillosis	Feb 96, Oct 95, Feb 93
Respiratory distress syndrome, adult	July 95, Oct 92, Feb 92
Respiratory failure	Oct 94, Oct 93, Oct 91
Bronchiectasis	Oct 93, Feb 93
Chest X-ray, abnormal	Oct 94, July 92
Emphysema	Oct 94, Feb 94
Lung function tests	July 94, Oct 92
Physiology, normal pulmonary	July 93, Oct 92
Pneumothorax	Feb 96, Feb 91
Sarcoidosis	Oct 93, July 92
SLE, pulmonary complications of	Feb 96, Oct 94
Transfer factor	July 94, Oct 93
Acute bronchiolitis	Oct 92
Alveolar hyperventilation	Feb 91
Asbestosis	July 92
Clubbing	Oct 91
Farmer's lung	Feb 91
Fibrosing alveolitis	July 93
Lung cancer, small cell	Feb 94
Lung cancer, surgery for	Feb 92
Oxygen therapy, long-term	July 94
Pancoast's tumour of lung	July 92
Psittacosis	Oct 91
Pulmonary cavitation	Feb 94
Pulmonary eosinophilia	Feb 95

RESPIRATORY DISEASE: REVISION CHECKLIST

Average 4 questions per exam. Numbers in brackets indicate the relative frequency of topics.

Respiratory infections
- ❑ Pneumonia (5)
- ❑ Broncho-pulmonary aspergillosis (3)
- ❑ Acute bronchiolitis
- ❑ Psittacosis
- ❑ Viral infections

Lung cancer
- ❑ Bronchial carcinoma (4)
- ❑ Pancoast's tumour
- ❑ Small cell cancer
- ❑ Surgery for cancer

Pulmonary physiology
- ❑ Lung function tests (2)
- ❑ Normal physiology (2)
- ❑ Transfer factor (2)

End-stage lung disease
- ❑ Respiratory failure (4)
- ❑ Long-term oxygen

Interstitial lung disease/fibrosis
- ❑ Extrinsic allergic alveolitis (4)
- ❑ ARDS (3)
- ❑ Bronchiectasis (2)
- ❑ Fibrosing alveolitis (2)
- ❑ Sarcoidosis (2)
- ❑ Asbestosis

Miscellaneous

- ❑ Sleep-apnoea syndrome (4)
- ❑ Asthma (3)
- ❑ Autoimmune disease and lung (3)
- ❑ Abnormal chest X-ray (2)
- ❑ Pneumothorax (2)
- ❑ Lung cavitation
- ❑ Pulmonary eosinophilia

February 1996
Polymyalgia rheumatica
Antiphospholipid syndrome

October 1995
SLE
Systemic sclerosis and the gut

July 1995
Behçet's disease
Hypertrophic osteoarthropathy

February 1995
Seropositive rheumatoid

October 1994
Rheumatoid arthritis
Vasculitic disease

July 1994
Polymyalgia rheumatica
Central nervous system abnormalities in SLE

February 1994
Features of Reiter's syndrome
Rheumatoid arthritis
Polymyositis

October 1993
SLE
Associations with ankylosing spondylitis
Neurological complications of rheumatoid arthritis
Reiter's disease

July 1993

Causes of peri-articular calcification
SLE

February 1993

Reiter's syndrome
Cranial arteritis

October 1992

Causes of arthralgia

July 1992

SLE

February 1992

Causes of arthritis
Wegener's granulomatosis

October 1991

Behçet's disease

February 1991

Seropostive rheumatoid arthritis
Polymyalgia rheumatica
Digital gangrene

RHEUMATOLOGY: TOPIC FREQUENCY INDEX

Rheumatoid arthritis	Feb 95, Oct 94, Feb 94, Oct 93, Feb 92, Feb 91
SLE	Oct 95, Oct 94, July 94, Oct 93, July 93, July 92
Polymyalgia rheumatica	Feb 96, July 94, Feb 91
Reiter's syndrome	Feb 94, Oct 93, Feb 93
Antiphospholipid syndrome	Feb 96, Feb 95
Behçet's disease	July 95, Oct 91
Ankylosing spondylitis	Oct 93
Arthralgia	Oct 92
Cranial arteritis	Feb 93
Digital gangrene	Feb 91
Hypertrophic osteoarthropathy	July 95
Peri-articular calcification	July 93
Systemic sclerosis	Oct 95
Vasculitic disease	Oct 94
Wegener's granulomatosis	Feb 92

RHEUMATOLOGY: REVISION CHECKLIST

Average 2 questions per exam. Numbers in brackets indicate the relative frequency of topics.

Auto-immune disease

- ❑ Rheumatoid arthritis (6)
- ❑ SLE (6)
- ❑ Wegener's granulomatosis

Other vasculitides

- ❑ Polymyalgia rheumatica (3)
- ❑ Cranial arteritis
- ❑ Vasculitic disease

Other arthritides

- ❑ Reiter's syndrome (3)
- ❑ Behçet's disease (2)
- ❑ Ankylosing spondylitis
- ❑ Arthralgia
- ❑ Hypertrophic osteo-arthropathy

Miscellaneous

- ❑ Anti-phospholipid syndrome (2)
- ❑ Digital gangrene
- ❑ Peri-articular calcification
- ❑ Systemic sclerosis

STATISTICS: EXAM TOPICS

February 1996
Normal distribution

October 1995
Standard deviation

February 1995
Significance tests

October 1994
Features of a normal distribution

July 1994
Statistical tests in a normal distribution

February 1994
Skewed distribution

October 1993
Specificity of clinical trials

July 1993
Chi-squared test

February 1993
Tests of significance

October 1992
Standard deviation

February 1992
Tests of significance

October 1991
Significance tests

February 1991
Normal distribution

STATISTICS: TOPIC FREQUENCY INDEX

Normal distribution	Feb 96, Oct 94, July 94, Feb 91
Significance tests	Feb 95, Feb 93, Feb 92, Oct 91
Standard deviation	Oct 95, Oct 92
Chi-squared test	July 93
Skewed distribution	Feb 94
Specificity of clinical trials	Oct 93

STATISTICS: REVISION CHECKLIST

Average 1 question per exam. Numbers in brackets indicate the relative frequency of topics.

Statistical populations

❑ Normal distribution (4)
❑ Standard deviation (2)
❑ Skewed distribution

Tests of significance

❑ Significance tests (4)
❑ Chi-square test

Miscellaneous

❑ Specificity of clinical trials

BOOKS FOR MRCP PART 1 FROM PASTEST

PasTest are the leading independent specialists in post-graduate medical education. We publish a wide range of revision books including:

MCQs in Basic Medical Sciences for MRCP 1
300 exam-based MCQs with correct answers and detailed explanatory notes

MRCP 1 Practice Exams: 2nd edition
Five complete MCQ Papers (300 MCQs) covering favourite Royal College topics

MRCP 1 MCQ Revision Book: 3rd edition
300 MCQs arranged by subject with correct answers and teaching notes, plus one complete mock exam

MRCP 1 MCQs with Individual Subject Summaries
200 exam-based MCQs with correct answers and informative subject summaries

Explanations to the RCP Past Papers
Correct answers and teaching notes related to the Royal College Green and Blue books of actual past exam questions

MRCP Part 1 MCQ Pocket Books
Each pocket-sized book contains 100 MCQs on favourite Membership topics

MRCP Part 1 Paediatric MCQ Revision Book
Over 300 new MCQs based on recent exam questions plus one complete practice exam

Explanations to the Royal College Red Booklet
Invaluable explanations to the RCP Red Book of MRCP Part 1 Paediatric questions

For full details of all our revision books contact PasTest today on **01565 755226** for a free copy of our current book catalogue and price list. Books sent by return of post worldwide.

PASTEST INTENSIVE COURSES FOR MRCP PART 1

For over 24 years PasTest, the leading independent specialists in postgraduate medical education, have been delivering top quality courses which have helped many thousands of doctors to pass the demanding MRCP Part 1 examination.

PasTest MRCP Part 1 courses are

- ✔ Intensive, practical and exam oriented
- ✔ Designed to strengthen exam technique
- ✔ Interactive and entertaining
- ✔ The key to exam success

Our reputation is built on results. With the official Royal College pass rate at 35%, PasTest delegates consistently achieve a pass rate of well over 60%. This is a competitive edge that you cannot afford to ignore.

Our MRCP Part 1 revision courses run three times a year in a wide range of venues including London, Manchester, Bristol, Glasgow, Dublin and Hong Kong.

For full details of the range of PasTest books and courses available for MRCP Part 1 candidates, contact PasTest today:

PasTest, Dept. PTB, Egerton Court, Parkgate Estate, Knutsford, Cheshire WA16 8DX

Tel: 01565 755226 Fax: 01565 650264
E-mail: pastest@dial.pipex.com